Problem Pages

A Book of Mathematical Problems for Upper Secondary School Students

D1634410

© The Mathematical Association 2000

All rights reserved. Unauthorised duplication contravenes applicable laws.

First published in 2000 by
The Mathematical Association
259 London Road
Leicester LE2 3BE
United Kingdom

ISBN 0 906588 45 6

Printed and bound in Great Britain at
J. W. Arrowsmith Ltd, Bristol.

Typeset by Bill Richardson

Introduction

This is a book of over sixty problems, together with suggested solutions. The problems are all accessible to students on A level or Scottish Higher courses, although many can be solved using mathematics covered lower down the school.

The problems are designed to stimulate interest and we hope that anyone in danger of being bored by Mathematics will be fascinated to find surprisingly simple and elegant solutions to what look like involved questions – solutions often so short and neat that they will stick in the memory. All of the problems encourage the development of problem-solving skills and should 'hook' students into hunting for a solution, helping them to develop the most important problem-solving skill of all – tenacity. Many of the problems require a degree of lateral thinking and should help to develop a sense of wonder at the power of Mathematics – when you know how! Questions which one cannot see how to do at first, or at all, yield solutions to surprise and delight. Very few solutions require more than a dozen lines and many need only five or six. We would not claim that many of the problems are new, but they make a fine collection for use in a variety of situations.

It is intended that the problems and solutions should be photocopied to allow their use to be as flexible as possible. Permission is given by The Mathematical Association to allow purchasers to make photocopies for use in their institutions.

Acknowledgements

This book of problems has been problems has been produced by the A and A/S level Subcommittee of the Teaching Committee of The Mathematical Association, and has been edited by Stephen Drape and Charlie Stripp.

The members of the Subcommittee who have contributed to the book are:

Barbara Cullingworth   Doug French   Sally Tavemer
Stephen Drape   Christine Lawley   Peter Thomas
Rosemary Emanuel   Jenny Orton   Marion Want
David Forster   Charlie Stripp

Other publications by this group include:

PIG and Other Tales, a book of mathematical readings with questions, suitable for sixth fomers.

Are You Sure? – Learning about Proof, a book of ideas for teachers of upper secondary school students.

Using this book

The book can provide a weekly problem over a two year cycle.

The problems can be used in a variety of ways. A method which has been tried successfully is to post up a problem each week in the classroom and invite students to work on it in their own time. Working together and discussing the problems should certainly be encouraged. The suggested solution can be posted up the following week, together with a new problem. Students' solutions can be displayed and alternative correct solutions can be a rich source of discussion. Many of the problems have a link to the standard curriculum, so they can be incorporated as an enhancement of normal teaching. The problems could form the basis of a student competition.

On the contents page each problem is given a level of difficulty ranging from 0, which is accessible to a GCSE level pupil, to 3 which is hard and will require a degree of inspiration. The problems are not presented in order of difficulty and are suitable for use in any order. Any difficulty rating is inevitably subjective and users may well disagree with some of our judgements.

Contents

Problem

Alphabetical Algebra

Suppose that

$$a = 1, b = 2, \ldots, z = 26$$

Evaluate the expression below:

$$(n - a)(n - b)\ldots(n - z)$$

Problem 1

Solution

Alphabetical Algebra

The expression simplifies to 0.

Any expression which has zero as a factor must equal zero:

$$(n - n)$$

(Did you multiply out?!!)

Problem

Suppose that

$$a = 1, b = 2, \ldots, z = 26$$

Evaluate the expression below:

$$(n - a)(n - b)\ldots(n - z)$$

Solution 1

Problem

Spot the Error

Look at the following argument:

$$\text{Let} \qquad x = y$$

$-y$ $\qquad \Rightarrow \qquad x - y = 0 \qquad$ [A]

$\times 2$ $\qquad \Rightarrow \qquad 2x - 2y = 0 \qquad$ [B]

Equate [A] and [B]

$$\Rightarrow \qquad x - y = 2x - 2y$$

Factorise the RHS

$$\Rightarrow \qquad (x - y) = 2(x - y)$$

$\div (x - y)$ $\qquad \Rightarrow \qquad 1 = 2$

Obviously, something must have gone wrong.
Can you find the mistake?

Problem 2

Solution

Spot the Error

Since $x = y$ then $x - y = 0$.

So dividing by $(x - y)$ means dividing by 0 which is an undefined operation in Mathematics.

The argument can be altered to make any pair of numbers appear to be equal to each other.

$$\text{e.g.} \quad 10 \times 0 = 12 \times 0$$

$$(\div 0) \quad 10 = 12$$

Problem

Look at the following argument:

	Let	$x = y$	
$-y$	$\Rightarrow$	$x - y = 0$	[A]
$\times 2$	$\Rightarrow$	$2x - 2y = 0$	[B]
Equate [A] and [B]	$\Rightarrow$	$x - y = 2x - 2y$	
Factorise the RHS	$\Rightarrow$	$(x - y) = 2(x - y)$	
$\div (x - y)$	$\Rightarrow$	$1 = 2$	

Obviously, something must have gone wrong.
Can you find the mistake?

Solution 2

Problem

Who's left standing?

Twenty people are standing in a circle.

The first person is asked to sit down and then every second person is told to sit down until there is one person left.

(ie. 1st sits down, then 3rd, 5th, …)

Which person is left standing?

What about for 100 people?

   n people?

Problem 3

Solution

Who's left standing?

For 20 people, the 8th person is left standing.
For 100 people, the 72nd person is left standing.

Generally:
For 2^p (where p is a positive integer), the 2^p th person is left standing.

Reason: first those which are not multiples of 2 sit down, then those which are not multiple of 4 etc.

For $2^p + 1$, the 2nd person is left standing.

For $2^p + 2$, the 4th person is left standing.

For $2^p + a$, the $2a$ th person is left standing (where $a < 2^p$).
In general, for n people, let p be the number such that

$$2^p < n \leqslant 2^{p+1}$$

Person left standing is $2(n - 2^p)$. [Can you prove this?]

| For 20, | $16 < 20 < 32$, | answer $= 2(20 - 16) = 8$ |
| For 100, | $64 < 100 < 128$, | answer $= 2(100 - 64) = 72$ |

Problem

Twenty people are standing in a circle.
The first person is asked to sit down and then every second person is told to sit down until there is one person left.
Which person is left standing?
What about for 100 people? n people?

Solution 3

Problem

How many primes?

Consider the nine-digit numbers formed by using each of the digits 1 to 9 once and only once.

     e.g.   145673928

              938267145

How many of these numbers are prime?

Problem 4

Solution

How many primes?

There are no prime numbers.

Add up the digits of each of the numbers and you get a total of 45 – which is divisible by 9.

Any number whose digit sum is divisible by 9 is itself divisible by 9 [can you prove this?].

This means that each of the 9! (362880) nine digit numbers is divisible by 9.

Therefore they are not prime.

Problem

Consider the nine-digit numbers formed by using each of the digits 1 to 9 once and only once.

e.g.   145673928
           938267145

How many of these numbers are prime?

Solution 4

Problem

Magical Multiplication

Take any 3 digit number.

Multiply it by 13

then multiply by 7

and then by 11.

What do you notice?

Does this always happen?

Why?

Problem 5

Solution

Magical Multiplication

Example $375 \times 13 \times 7 \times 11 = 375375$

This happens for all 3 digit numbers.

This is because

$$13 \times 7 \times 11 = 1001$$

and $1001 \times abc$ $= 1000abc + abc$

$$= abc000 + abc$$

$$= abcabc$$

Problem

Take any 3 digit number.

Multiply it by 13

then multiply by 7

and then by 11.

What do you notice?

Does this always happen?

Why?

Solution 5

Problem

Replicating Numbers

Make the numbers in this list below by using only the digits contained in each number (each digit can only be used once).

You can use any mathematical symbols and operations.

a)   125

b)   128

c)   216

d)   625

Problem 6

Solution

Replicating Numbers

Suggested answers are:

$$a) \qquad 125 = 5^{(2+1)}$$

$$b) \qquad 128 = 2^{(8-1)}$$

$$c) \qquad 216 = 6^{(2+1)}$$

$$d) \qquad 625 = 5^{(6-2)}$$

Problem

Make the numbers in this list below by using only the digits contained in each number (each digit can only be used once).

You can use any mathematical symbols and operations.

a) 125   b) 128   c) 216   d) 625

Solution 6

Problem

Replicating Numbers - Take Two

Make the numbers in this list below by using only the digits contained in each number (each digit can only be used once).

You can use any Mathematical symbols and operations.

a)   3125

b)   4096

c)   16807

d)   20736 (hard!)

e)   32768

Problem 7

Solution

Replicating Numbers - Take Two

Suggested answers are

a) $\quad 3125 = 5^{[(2 + 3) \times 1]}$

b) $\quad 4096 = 4^{[(0 \times 9) + 6]}$

c) $\quad 16807 = 7^{[(6 - 1) + (8 \times 0)]}$

d) $\quad 20736 = (6 \times 2)^{(7 - 3 - 0)}$

e) $\quad 32768 = 8^{[(3 + 2) \times (7 - 6)]}$

Problem

Make the numbers in this list below by using only the digits contained in each number (each digit can only be used once).

You can use any mathematical symbols and operations.

a) 3125   b) 4096   c) 16807   d) 20736   e) 32768

Solution 7

Problem

4 Fours

Try to make each of the numbers 0 to 25 using the number 4 exactly four times.

You are allowed to use any mathematical symbols and operations.

e.g. $43 = 44 - \dfrac{4}{4}$

Solution

4 Fours

Here are some selected answers:

$$0 = (4 - 4) \times (4 + 4)$$

$$5 = \frac{(4 \times 4) + 4}{4}$$

$$10 = \frac{44 - 4}{4}$$

$$13 = \frac{4!}{\sqrt{4}} + \frac{4}{4}$$

$$18 = 4! - 4 - 4 + \sqrt{4}$$

$$25 = 4! + \frac{4}{\sqrt{4} \times \sqrt{4}}$$

Problem

Try to make each of the numbers 0 to 25 using the number 4 exactly four times.

You are allowed to use any mathematical symbols and operations.

Solution 8

Problem

Diagonal Crossings

Show that the diagonals of a rhombus ~~cross~~ at right
angles.

bisect each
other
∧

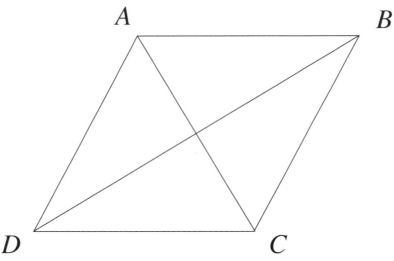

Problem 9

Solution

Diagonal Crossings

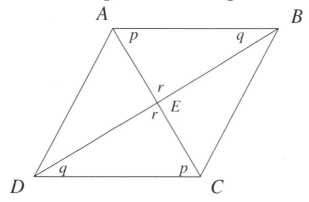

$$\angle EAB \ = \ \angle ECD \ = \ p \qquad \text{(alternate angles)}$$

$$\text{and } \angle EBA \ = \ \angle EDC \ = \ q \qquad \text{(alternate angles)}$$

Since $AB \ = \ DC$, $\triangle AEB \ \equiv \ \triangle DEC$ ($\equiv$ means congruent).

So, $DE \ = \ EB$ and $AE \ = \ EC$.

Therefore $\triangle AED \ \equiv \ \triangle CEB \ \equiv \ \triangle AEB \ \equiv \ \triangle DEC$.

Therefore the 4 angles around E are equal to $90°$.

Problem
Show that the diagonals of a rhombus cross at right angles.

Solution 9

Problem

Creating Space

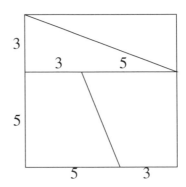

Cut up an 8cm by 8cm
square as shown:

Rearrange the pieces into the rectangle shown:

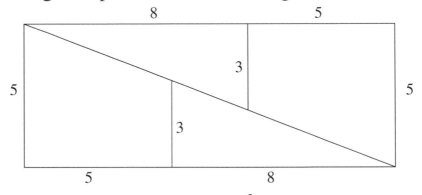

The square has an area of 64cm^2 and the rectangle has
an area of 65cm^2 – explain this apparent contradiction.

Problem 10

Solution

Creating Space

There actually is no contradiction.

Along the diagonal of the rectangle is small, narrow parallelogram of area 1cm².

You can see that the pieces don't actually fit by looking at the gradients of the lines or considering similar triangles.

[The triangle in the original square has a gradient of $3/8 = 0.375$ and the diagonal of the 'rectangle' has a gradient of $5/13 = 0.385$ (3sf).]

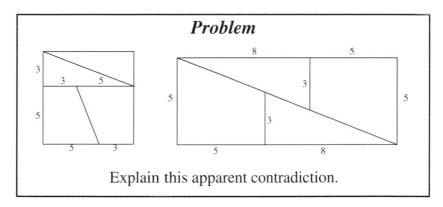

Problem

Explain this apparent contradiction.

Solution 10

Problem

Around the world

Luke and Leah wanted to measure the circumference of the Earth. They both had very long tape measures.

Luke measured the planet at the surface, but Leah measured at a height of 1 metre above the surface.

What is the difference in metres between Luke's and Leah's measurements?

Problem 11

Solution

Around the world

Let R be the radius of the Earth.

Luke measures $2\pi R$.

Leah measures $2\pi(R + 1)$.

The exact difference is $2\pi(R + 1) - 2\pi R = 2\pi$ which is about 6 metres.

Problem

Luke and Leah wanted to measure the circumference of the Earth. They both had very long tape measures.

Luke measured the planet at the surface, but Leah measured at a height of 1 metre above the surface.

What is the difference in metres between Luke's and Leah's measurements?

Solution 11

Problem

A Fraction of Pythagoras

If you work out $\dfrac{1}{3} + \dfrac{1}{5}$, you will get $\dfrac{8}{15}$.

The two parts of this fraction form the two smallest numbers in a Pythagorean triple

$$\text{i.e. } 8^2 + 15^2 = 17^2.$$

Try another pair of fractions with consecutive odd numbers as their denominators.

Does it work again?

Explain why.

What happens if the denominators are two consecutive even numbers?

Problem 12

Solution

A Fraction of Pythagoras

Let the 2 fractions be $\frac{1}{n}$ and $\frac{1}{n+2}$, then they are added as follows:

$$\frac{1}{n} + \frac{1}{n+2} = \frac{n+2+n}{n(n+2)} = \frac{2n+2}{n(n+2)}.$$

Squaring and adding the numerator and denominator:

$$(2n+2)^2 + (n(n+2))^2 = 4n^2 + 8n + 4 + n^2(n^2 + 4n + 4)$$
$$= n^4 + 4n^3 + 8n^2 + 8n + 4$$
$$= (n^2 + 2n + 2)^2$$

which is of the form $a^2 + b^2 = c^2$ so the numbers formed in this way will always make Pythagorean triples.

Note: The result above did not specify that n must be odd so the same result holds for even numbers but these fractions will have a factor 2 to be cancelled.

Problem

If you work out $\frac{1}{3} + \frac{1}{5}$, you will get $\frac{8}{15}$.

The two parts of this fraction form the two smallest numbers in a Pythagorean triple i.e. $8^2 + 15^2 = 17^2$.

Try another pair of fractions with consecutive odd numbers as their denominators. Does it work again?

Explain why.

What happens if the denominators are two consecutive even numbers?

Solution 12

Problem

Just one dimension

Look at the shape below (called an *annulus*).

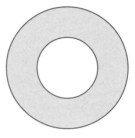

Find the single measurement from which the area of the annulus can be calculated.

Problem 13

Solution

Just one dimension

Let the small circle have radius r and the larger have radius R.

The shaded area is $\pi\left(R^2 - r^2\right)$.

How can this be obtained using one measurement?

Draw the line shown, which is a tangent to the inner circle, and represent its length by H.

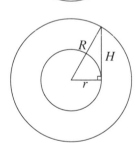

The triangle is right-angled since the tangent is perpendicular to a radius. So, by Pythagoras, $H^2 = R^2 - r^2$ and the area is πH^2.

Problem

Look at the shape alongside (called an annulus).

Find the single measurement from which the area of the annulus can be calculated.

Solution 13

Problem

The Root of the Matter

Work out:

$$\sqrt{(1 \times 2 \times 3 \times 4) + 1}$$

$$\sqrt{(2 \times 3 \times 4 \times 5) + 1}$$

$$\sqrt{(3 \times 4 \times 5 \times 6) + 1}$$

$$\sqrt{(4 \times 5 \times 6 \times 7) + 1}$$

You should find that you obtain whole number answers.

Prove that this is ALWAYS the case.

Problem 14

Solution

The Root of the Matter

$$\sqrt{(1 \times 2 \times 3 \times 4) + 1} = \sqrt{25} = 5$$

$$\sqrt{(2 \times 3 \times 4 \times 5) + 1} = \sqrt{121} = 11$$

$$\sqrt{(3 \times 4 \times 5 \times 6) + 1} = \sqrt{361} = 19$$

$$\sqrt{(4 \times 5 \times 6 \times 7) + 1} = \sqrt{841} = 29$$

Representing the numbers in the obvious way, in general the expression under the square root is

$$n(n + 1)(n + 2)(n + 3) + 1$$

$$= n^4 + 6n^3 + 11n^2 + 6n + 1$$

$$= \left(n^2 + 3n + 1\right)^2.$$

So the result is always an integer.

Problem

Work out:

$$\sqrt{(1 \times 2 \times 3 \times 4) + 1}; \ \sqrt{(2 \times 3 \times 4 \times 5) + 1}$$

$$\sqrt{(3 \times 4 \times 5 \times 6) + 1}; \ \sqrt{(4 \times 5 \times 6 \times 7) + 1}$$

You should find that you obtain whole number answers.
Prove that this is ALWAYS the case.

Solution 14

Problem

Calculator Trouble

You have a faulty calculator.

The only functions that work properly are:

        x^2

Can you find a sequence of calculator operations to multiply two numbers together using this calculator?

Problem 15

Solution

Calculator Trouble

Let x and y be the two numbers.

Twice the product can be obtained by using the following expression:

$$2xy = (x + y)^2 - x^2 - y^2$$

Halving a number can be done by using the expression below:

$$\tfrac{1}{2}z = (z + 0.25)^2 - z^2 - (0.25)^2.$$

eg. $x = 4$, $y = 5$
$2xy = (4 + 5)^2 - 4^2 - 5^2 = 81 - 16 = 25 = 40$
Let $z = 40$

$\tfrac{1}{2}z = (40 + 0.25)^2 - 40^2 - 0.25^2$

$= 1620.25 - 1600 - 0.25 = 20$ the required answer

Problem

You have a faulty calculator. The only functions that work properly are: $\boxed{+}$, $\boxed{-}$, $\boxed{x^2}$.

Can you find a sequence of calculator operations to multiply two numbers together using this calculator?

Solution 15

Problem

Up the Pole

Consider two poles whose tops are 3 metres and 2 metres above the ground.

The top of each pole is attached to the bottom of the other by rope.

Prove that the ropes will always cross at a certain height (which should be calculated).

Problem 16

Solution

Up the Pole

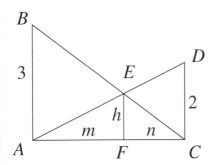

AB and *CD* are the poles.

$\triangle ABC$ is similar to $\triangle FEC$.

So $\dfrac{3}{m+n} = \dfrac{h}{n}$.

In the same way,

$$\dfrac{2}{m+n} = \dfrac{h}{m}.$$

So $\dfrac{m}{n} = \dfrac{3}{2}$ and $h = \dfrac{2m}{m+n}$.

$\dfrac{1}{h} = \dfrac{m+n}{2m} = \dfrac{1}{2} + \dfrac{1}{2}\left(\dfrac{n}{m}\right)$.

$\dfrac{1}{h} = \dfrac{1}{2} + \dfrac{1}{3} = \dfrac{5}{6}$.

So $h = 6/5 = 1{\cdot}2$.

So the height is always 1.2m

Problem

Consider two poles whose tops are 3 metres and 2 metres above the ground. The top of each pole is attached to the bottom of the other by rope.

Prove that the ropes will always cross at a certain height (which should be calculated).

Solution 16

Problem

Neighbours

Show that the sum of 3 consecutive numbers in an arithmetic sequence is three times the middle term.

*(An **arithmetic** sequence is one in which each pair of consecutive terms has a common difference.)*

Solution

Neighbours

The 3 numbers can be written as:

$$a \qquad a + d \qquad a + 2d$$

where a is the first term and d is the common difference.

The sum is equal to

$$a + (a + d) + (a + 2d)$$

$$= 3a + 3d$$

$$= 3(a + d)$$

Problem

Show that the sum of 3 consecutive numbers in an arithmetic sequence is three times the middle term.

*(An **arithmetic** sequence is one in which each pair of consecutive terms has a common difference.)*

Solution 17

Problem

Neighbours II

Show that the product of 3 consecutive numbers in a geometric sequence is equal to the cube of the middle term.

*(A **geometric** sequence is one in which each pair of consecutive terms has a common ratio.)*

Problem 18

Solution

Neighbours II

The 3 numbers can be written as

$$a \qquad ar \qquad ar^2$$

where a is the first term and r is the common ratio.

The product is equal to

$$a \times ar \times ar^2$$

$$= a^3 \times r^3$$

$$= (ar)^3$$

Problem

Show that the product of 3 consecutive numbers in a geometric sequence is equal to the cube of the middle term.

*(A **geometric** sequence is one in which each pair of consecutive terms has a common ratio.)*

Solution 18

Problem

Turn add turnabout

Take any 2 digit number.

Reverse the digits and add together your number and the reversed number.

e.g.   24 – reversed gives 42   24 + 42 = 66
          92 – reversed gives 29   92 + 29 = 121

What do you notice about the answer?

Is it always true?

Can you show why?

Problem 19

Solution

Turn add turnabout

The answer is always a multiple of 11.

Reason

Let the number be $\quad 10x + y$

Reversed it gives $\quad 10y + x$

Adding these together gives:

$$(10x + y) + (10y + x) = 11x + 11y$$
$$= 11(x + y)$$

which is a multiple of 11.

Problem

Take any 2 digit number.

Reverse the digits and add together your number and the reversed number.

e.g. $\quad$ 24 – reversed gives 42 $\qquad$ 24 + 42 = 66

$\qquad$ 92 – reversed gives 29 $\qquad$ 92 + 29 = 121

What do you notice about the answer? Is it always true? Can you show why?

Solution 19

Problem

Turn take turnabout

Take a 2 digit number, then reverse it.

Take the smaller away from the larger.

e.g.   26 – reversed gives 62   62 – 26 = 36
         71 – reversed gives 17   71 – 17 = 54

What do you notice about the answer?

Is it always true?

Can you explain why?

Problem 20

Solution

Turn take turnabout

The answer is always a multiple of 9.

Reason

Let the number be $\quad 10x + y$ (and suppose $x > y$).

Reversed it gives $\quad 10y + x$.

Subtracting these gives:

$$(10x + y) - (10y + x) = 9x - 9y$$
$$= 9(x - y)$$

which is a multiple of 9.

Problem

Take a 2 digit number, then reverse it.

Take the smaller away from the larger.

e.g.   26 – reversed gives 62 $62 - 26 = 36$

           71 – reversed gives 17 $71 - 17 = 54$

What do you notice about the answer? Is it always true?

Can you explain why?

Solution 20

Problem

Turn take turnabout (the sequel)

Take a 3 digit number, then reverse it.
Take the smaller away from the larger.

e.g.　276 – reversed gives 672　672 – 276 = 396
　　　845 – reversed gives 548　845 –548 = 297

What do you notice about the answer?

It is always true?

Can you explain why?

Problem 21

Solution

Turn take turnabout (the sequel)

The answer is always a multiple of 9 and of 11 (hence it is a multiple of 99).

Reason

Let the number be $100x + 10y + z$ (with $x > z$).

Reversed it gives $100z + 10y + x$.

Subtracting these gives:

$$(100x + 10y + z) - (100z + 10y + x) = 99x - 99z$$
$$= 99(x - z)$$
$$= 9 \times 11(x - z)$$

which is a multiple of 9 and of 11.

Problem

Take a 3 digit number, then reverse it. Take the smaller away from the larger.

e.g. 276 – reversed gives 672 $672 - 276 = 396$
            845 – reversed gives 548 $845 - 548 = 297$

What do you notice about the answer? It is always true?
Can you explain why?

Solution 21

Problem

What you say is what you get!

Find the next 2 lines in this sequence:

1

11

21

1211

111221

312211

Problem 22

Solution

What you say is what you get!

This sequence is a case of say what you see.

The first line has one 1 (ie. 11)

The second line has two 1s (ie.21)

The third line has one 2 and one 1 (ie.1211)

The fourth line has one 1, one 2 and two 1s (ie. 111221)

The fifth line has three 1s, two 2s and one 1 (ie. 312211)

The sixth line has one 3, one 1, two 2s and two 1s, so the seventh line will be **13112221.**

The seventh line has one 1, one 3, two 1s, three 2s and one 1, so the eight line will be **1113213211**

Problem

Find the next 2 terms in this sequence:

1; 11; 21; 1211; 111221; 312211

Solution 22

Problem

Area = Perimeter

How many non-congruent right-angled triangles are there for which the length of the perimeter, in cm, and the area of the interior, in cm², are numerically equal? The lengths of the sides are integers.

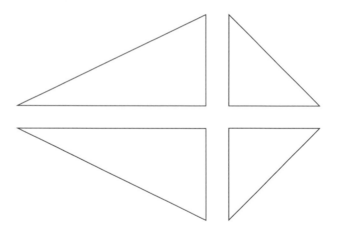

Problem 23

Solution

Area = Perimeter

Let the lengths of the shorter sides be x cm and y cm then the other side is: $\sqrt{x^2 + y^2}$.

The first condition can then be expressed as an equation: $\sqrt{x^2 + y^2} + x + y = \frac{1}{2}xy$.

Rearraging and squaring both sides gives:

$$2xy - x^2y - xy^2 + \tfrac{1}{4}x^2y^2 = 0$$

$$\tfrac{1}{4}xy(8 - 4x - 4y + xy) = 0.$$

As x and y are positive, then $8 - 4x - 4y + xy = 0$.

So $y = \frac{4x-8}{x-4} = 4\left(\frac{x-2}{x-4}\right) = 4\left(1 + \frac{2}{x-4}\right)$ (if $x \neq 4$).

There are only **two** triangles that meet this condition:

$$(6, 8, 10) \text{ and } (5,12,13).$$

Problem

How many non-congruent right-angled triangles are there for which the length of the perimeter, in cm, and the area of the interior, in cm², are numerically equal? The lengths of the sides are integers.

Solution 23

Problem

Zeros to go!

100!
How many zeros are there after the last non-zero digit?

Remember:

$$100! = 100 \times 99 \times \ldots \times 2 \times 1$$

Solution

Zeros to go!

There are 24 zeros after the non-zero digit.

Reason

Each zero is obtained by multiplying a factor of 2 by a factor of 5.

There are 24 factors of 5 (one for each multiple of 5 and one extra for each multiple of 25).

There are more multiples of 2 than multiples of 5, (at least 1 one more for each even number).

So there must be 24 zeros

In fact, 100! =   93 326 215 443 944 152 681 699 238 856 266 700 490 715 968 264 381 621 468 592 963 895 217 599 993 229 915 608 941 463 976 156 518 286 253 697 920 827 223 758 251 185 210 916 864 000 000 000 000 000 000 000 000

Problem

100!

How many zeros are there after the last non-zero digit?

Remember: 100! = 100 × 99 × ... × 2 × 1

Solution 24

Problem

Fractions forever!

What is the value of

$$\frac{1}{2} +$$

$$\left(\frac{1}{3} + \frac{2}{3}\right) +$$

$$\left(\frac{1}{4} + \frac{2}{4} + \frac{3}{4}\right) +$$

$$\left(\frac{1}{5} + \frac{2}{5} + \frac{3}{5} + \frac{4}{5}\right) +$$

$$\ldots +$$

$$\left(\frac{1}{100} + \frac{2}{100} + \ldots + \frac{98}{100} + \frac{99}{100}\right)?$$

Problem 25

Solution

Fractions forever!

$$\frac{1}{2} + \left(\frac{1}{3} + \frac{2}{3}\right) + \left(\frac{1}{4} + \frac{2}{4} + \frac{3}{4}\right) + \ldots \left(\frac{1}{100} + \frac{2}{100} + \ldots + \frac{98}{100} + \frac{99}{100}\right)$$

$$= \sum_{n=2}^{100} \left(\sum_{m=1}^{n-1} \frac{m}{n} \right)$$

$$= \sum_{n=2}^{100} \left(\frac{1}{n} \sum_{m=1}^{n-1} m \right) \qquad [n \text{ is a constant in the inner sum}]$$

$$= \sum_{n=2}^{100} \left(\frac{1}{n} \cdot \frac{1}{2}(n-1)n \right) \quad [\text{using the sum of consecutive integers}]$$

$$= \frac{1}{2} \sum_{n=2}^{100} (n-1) \qquad [\text{cancelling } n]$$

$$= \frac{1}{2} \sum_{i=1}^{99} i \qquad\qquad [\text{sub } i = n-1]$$

$$= \tfrac{1}{2} \times \tfrac{1}{2} \times 99 \times 100 \quad [\text{using the sum of integers}]$$

$$= \mathbf{2475}$$

Problem

What is the value of

$$\frac{1}{2} + \left(\frac{1}{3} + \frac{2}{3}\right) + \left(\frac{1}{4} + \frac{2}{4} + \frac{3}{4}\right) + \ldots \left(\frac{1}{100} + \frac{2}{100} + \ldots + \frac{98}{100} + \frac{99}{100}\right) ?$$

Solution 25

Problem

Painted Cube

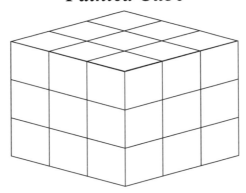

A wooden cube with edges of length n units (where n is an integer greater than 2) is painted black all over. By slices parallel to its faces, the cube is cut into n^3 smaller cubes each with edges of length 1 unit.

The number of smaller cubes with one face painted black is equal to the number of smaller cubes completely free of paint.

What is the value of n?

Problem 26

Solution

Painted Cube

The number of smaller cubes with one face painted black is $6(n-2)^2$.

The number of smaller cubes completely free of paint is $(n-2)^3$.

Equating these two expressions gives

$$6(n-2)^2 = (n-2)^3.$$

$n > 2 \Rightarrow (n-2) \neq 0$, so we can divide by $(n-2)^2$

$$\text{so} \quad 6 = n - 2$$
$$\text{and } n = 8.$$

Problem

A wooden cube with edges of length n units (where n is an integer greater than 2) is painted black all over. By slices parallel to its faces, the cube is cut into n^3 smaller cubes each with edges of length 1 unit.

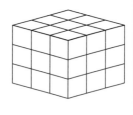

The number of smaller cubes with one face painted black is equal to the number of smaller cubes completely free of paint.

What is the value of n?

Solution 26

Problem

Seven Up

Consider a 3 digit number

$$A = 100a + 10b + c$$

(a, b, c are the digits of A)

Prove that A is divisible by 7 if $2a + 10b + c$ is divisible by 7.

Solution

Seven Up

Suppose that $2a + 10b + c$ is divisible by 7.
So there must be an integer k such that

$$2a + 10b + c = 7k.$$

But $100a = 98a + 2a = 7 \times 14a + 2a$.
So $98a + 2a + 10b + c = 98a + 7k$

$$100a + 10b + c = 7(14a + k).$$

As $A = 100a + 10b + c$, it follows that A must be divisible by 7.

Problem

Consider a 3 digit number

$$A = 100a + 10b + c$$

$$(a, b, c \text{ are the digits of } A)$$

Prove that A is divisible by 7 if $2a + 10b + c$ is divisible by 7.

Solution 27

Problem

Semi-Circles

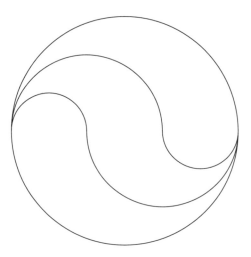

In the diagram above, the semi-circles have radii of lengths 1cm, 2cm and 3cm.

Find the ratio of areas of the 3 regions into which the circle is divided.

Solution

Semi-Circles

The areas of the semi-circles are $\frac{1}{2}\pi$, 2π, $4\frac{1}{2}\pi$.

Ratio of areas

$$\frac{1}{2}\pi + 4\frac{1}{2}\pi - 2\pi \ : \ 2\left(2\pi - \frac{1}{2}\pi\right) \ : \ \frac{1}{2}\pi + 4\frac{1}{2}\pi - 2\pi$$

$$= \qquad 1 \qquad : \qquad 1 \qquad : \qquad 1$$

Problem

In the diagram, the semi-circles have radii of lengths 1cm, 2cm and 3cm.

Find the ratio of areas of the 3 regions into which the circle is divided.

Problem

A4 Paper

An A4 sheet of paper is such that if you fold the paper in half (fold parallel to the width), you will get a rectangular sheet of paper (an A5 sheet) which is similar to the original A4 sheet.

Given this fact, find the ratio

width : length

Problem 29

Solution

A4 Paper

BC is the width of the A4 sheet (*y*).

AB is the length of the A4 sheet (2*x*).

E is the midpoint of *AB*.

F is the midpoint of *DC*.

AE is the width of the A5 sheet (*x*).

EF is the length of the A5 sheet (*y*).

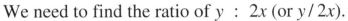

We need to find the ratio of *y* : 2*x* (or *y* / 2*x*).

By similarity, the ratios of width : length will be the same in both sheets.

$$\frac{\text{width}}{\text{length}} = \frac{y}{2x} = \frac{x}{y}$$ The first ratio is for the A4 sheet and the second for the A5 sheet .

$$\text{gives } y^2 = 2x^2 \implies \left(\frac{y}{2x}\right)^2 = \frac{1}{2}$$

(Take the positive root as lengths are positive.)

So width : length = *y* : 2*x* = 1 : $\sqrt{2}$.

Problem

An A4 sheet of paper is such that if you fold the paper in half (fold parallel to the width), you will get a rectangular sheet of paper (an A5 sheet) which is similar to the original A4 sheet.

Given this fact, find the ratio   width : length

Solution 29

Problem

Circuit

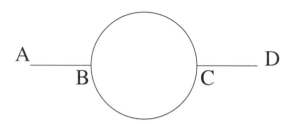

The probability of turning left at each junction is ½ and the probability of turning right is ½.

Once you arrive at A or D, you stop.

Find the probability of arriving at D if you start from A.

Problem 30

Solution

Circuit

Going $A \to B \to C \to D$ using just ½ circuit round the circle

$$\text{prob} = \tfrac{1}{2}$$

(second move must reach C, prob to reach D is ½)

$A \to B \to C \to B \to C \to D$ using 1½ circuits:

$$\text{prob} \;=\; \tfrac{1}{2} \times \tfrac{1}{2} \times \tfrac{1}{2} \;=\; \tfrac{1}{8}$$

Prob (2½ circuits) $= \tfrac{1}{32}$.

$$\text{Prob } (A \to D) = \tfrac{1}{2}\left(1 + \tfrac{1}{4} + \tfrac{1}{16} + \dots\right)$$

$$= \tfrac{1}{2} \times \tfrac{4}{3} \qquad \text{(a geometric progression)}$$

$$= \tfrac{2}{3}.$$

Problem

The probability of turning left at each junction is ½ and the probability of turning right is ½.

Once you arrive at A or D, you stop.

Find the probability of arriving at D if you start from A.

Solution 30

Problem

Adding Fractions

If you add the numerators and denominators of two distinct fractions, then the resulting fraction lies between the two original fractions.

$$\text{e.g. } \frac{1}{2} \text{ and } \frac{1}{3} \text{ give } \frac{1 + 1}{2 + 3} = \frac{2}{5}$$

$$\text{and } \frac{2}{5} \text{ lies between } \frac{1}{2} \text{ and } \frac{1}{3}.$$

Prove that, if

$$\frac{a}{b} < \frac{c}{d}, \text{ then } \frac{a}{b} < \frac{a + c}{b + d} < \frac{c}{d}$$

(a, b, c and d are positive integers).

Problem 31

Solution

Adding Fractions

Suppose that $\dfrac{a}{b} > \dfrac{a+c}{b+d}$, then $a(b+d) > b(a+c)$ and hence $ad > bc$.

This is a contradiction, since $\dfrac{a}{b} < \dfrac{c}{d}$ implies that $ad < bc$. Hence $\dfrac{a}{b} < \dfrac{a+c}{b+d}$.

$\dfrac{a+c}{b+d} < \dfrac{c}{d}$ can be proved similarly.

Problem

If you add the numerators and denominators of two distinct fractions, then the resulting fraction lies between the two original fractions.

Prove that, if

$$\frac{a}{b} < \frac{c}{d}, \text{ then } \frac{a}{b} < \frac{a+c}{b+d} < \frac{c}{d}$$

(a, b, c and d are positive integers).

Problem

One More

What is the first square number in the sequence:

$$1, 11, 111, 1111, ... \ ?$$

Are there any more square numbers in the sequence?

Problem 32

Solution

One More

1 is the first square number.

If there is another square number in the sequence, then the unit digit of the number that is squared must be 1 or 9.

The number is of the form

$$(10n \pm 1)^2 = 100n^2 \pm 20n + 1$$
$$= 10(10n^2 \pm 2n) + 1$$

$10n^2 \pm 2n$ gives the 10s digit, but this number is an even number (so it can't be 1).

Hence, no further square numbers appear in the sequence.

Problem

What is the first square number in the sequence:

$$1, 11, 111, 1111, \ldots ?$$

Are there any more square numbers in the sequence?

Solution 32

Problem

Van Schooten

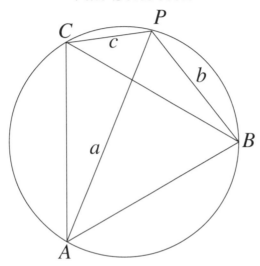

ABC is an equilateral triangle inscribed in a circle.

P is a point on the minor arc *BC*.

If $AP = a$, $BP = b$, $CP = c$, prove $a = b + c$ (Van Schooten's Theorem).

Solution

Van Schooten

$\angle APB = \angle APC = 60°$ (angles in the same segment)

Similarly, $\angle APC = 60° = \angle APC$.

Applying the cosine rule to triangles APB and APC:

Since $\cos 60° = \frac{1}{2}$,

$$AB^2 = a^2 + b^2 - ab \text{ and } AC^2 = a^2 + c^2 - ac.$$

Since $AB = AC$, $b^2 - ab = c^2 - ac$

$$b^2 - c^2 = ab - ac$$

$$(b - c)(b + c) = a(b - c)$$

$$b + c = a, \quad \text{provided } b \neq c.$$

In the case where $b = c$, the two triangles, APB and ABC are right-angled and $b = c = \frac{1}{2}a$, so the result still holds.

Problem

ABC is an equilateral triangle inscribed in a circle.

P is a point on the minor arc BC.

If $AP = a$, $BP = b$, $CP = c$, prove $a = b + c$ (Van Schooten's Theorem).

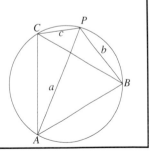

Solution 33

Problem

Find the area

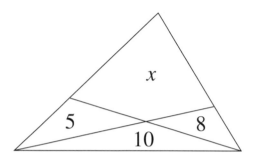

What is the area x?

Solution

Find the area

This proof makes frequent use of
the result that the ratio of the
areas of triangles of equal height
is the same as the ratio of their
bases.

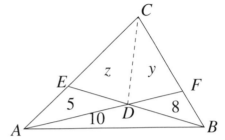

$$\frac{\triangle AFC}{\triangle AFB} = \frac{CF}{BF} = \frac{\triangle CDF}{\triangle BDF} \Rightarrow \frac{5 + y + z}{18} = \frac{y}{8}$$

$$\frac{\triangle CBE}{\triangle ABE} = \frac{CE}{AE} = \frac{\triangle CDE}{\triangle ADE} \Rightarrow \frac{8 + y + z}{15} = \frac{z}{5}$$

$$20 + 4y + 4z = 9y \Rightarrow 20 + 4z = 5y$$

$$8 + y + z = 3z \Rightarrow y = 2z - 8$$

$$20 + 4z = 5(2z - 8) \Rightarrow 6z = 60 \Rightarrow z = 10$$

giving $y = 12$ and so, $x = y + z = 22$.

Problem

What is the area x?

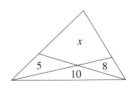

Solution 34

Problem

Integration

Let $I = \int \sin x \cos x \, dx$.

Using $u = \sin x$ gives $\dfrac{du}{dx} = \cos x \Rightarrow$

$$I = \int u \, du = \tfrac{1}{2}u^2 + k = \tfrac{1}{2}\sin^2 x + k.$$

Using $u = \cos x$ gives $\dfrac{du}{dx} = -\sin x \Rightarrow$

$$I = \int -u \, du = -\tfrac{1}{2}u^2 + c = -\tfrac{1}{2}\cos^2 x + c.$$

Both methods are valid, so both answers must be correct.

Prove that the answers are equivalent.

Problem 35

Solution

Integration

Using $I = \frac{1}{2}\sin^2 x + k$ and the identity $\cos^2 x + \sin^2 x = 1$ gives

$$I = \frac{1}{2}\left(1 - \cos^2 x\right) + k$$
$$= \frac{1}{2} - \frac{1}{2}\cos^2 x + k$$
$$= -\frac{1}{2}\cos^2 x + \frac{1}{2} + k$$

So the solutions are equivalent if $c = \frac{1}{2} + k$.

The "difference" is in the constant of integration.

It is interesting to examine the graphs of $y = \frac{1}{2}\sin^2 x$ and $y = -\frac{1}{2}\cos^2 x$ to see how this works.

Problem

Let $I = \int \sin x \cos x \, dx$. Using $u = \sin x$ gives $\frac{du}{dx} = \cos x$

$\Rightarrow I = \int u \, du = \frac{1}{2}u^2 + k = \frac{1}{2}\sin^2 x + k$.

Using $u = \cos x$ gives $\frac{du}{dx} = -\sin x \Rightarrow$

$I = \int -u \, du = -\frac{1}{2}u^2 + c = -\frac{1}{2}\cos^2 x + c$.

Both methods are valid, so both answers must be correct.

Prove that the answers are equivalent.

Solution 35

Problem

Mountains

A party of climbers are climbing Beinn Dubh.

At the top, looking across at Beinn Beag (2500 feet), which is 30 miles away, they see that Beinn Mhor (3000 feet), which is 60 miles away, is just showing over the top.

How high is Beinn Dubh?

Problem 36

Solution

Mountains

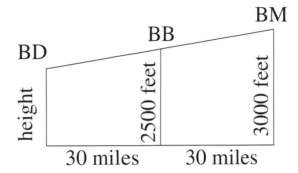

The tops of the mountains are denoted by their initials. BM is 30 miles from BB. So by congruent triangles, the difference in height between where the climbers are and the height of BB must be 500 feet.

Therefore, Beinn Dubh 2000 feet high.

Problem

A party of climbers are climbing Beinn Dubh.

At the top, looking across at Beinn Beag (2500 feet), which is 30 miles away, they see that Beinn Mhor (3000 feet), which is 60 miles away, is just showing over the top.

How high is Beinn Dubh?

Solution 36

Problem

Candles

Two cylindrical candles are of different heights.

The white one is 4 cm higher than the red one.

The white one burns down in 6 hours, the red one in 4 hours.

When the white one has burned for 4 hours, it is as high as when the red one has burned for 2½ hours.

What was the original height of each candle?

Solution

Candles

Let w be the original height of the white candle and let r be the original height of the red candle.

Initially, $w = r + 4$.

After 4 hours, $\frac{2}{3}$ of the white candle has burned (assuming a steady rate), so its height will be $\frac{1}{3}w$.

After $2\frac{1}{2}$ hours, the height of the red candle will be $\frac{3}{8}r$.

So $\qquad \frac{1}{3}w = \frac{3}{8}r \qquad \Rightarrow w = 1\frac{1}{8}r.$

Substituting in the original equations gives

$$1\frac{1}{8}r = r + 4 \qquad \Rightarrow \frac{1}{8}r = 4.$$

Hence the original height of the red candle is 32 cm and the original height of the white candle is 36 cm.

Problem

Two cylindrical candles are of different heights.

The white one is 4cm higher than the red one.

The white one burns down in 6 hours, the red one in 4 hours.

When the white one has burned for 4 hours, it is as high as when the red one has burned for 2½ hours.

What was the original height of each candle?

Solution 37

Problem

Miles Away

A driver notices that her milometer is showing a 5 digit palindromic number. She is astonished when, two hours further on her travels, the milometer is showing another palindromic number.

Find the different possible numbers of miles that she could have travelled.

Problem 38

Solution

Miles Away

The number of miles travelled in 2 hours is likely to be around 100.

There are 3 cases.

Case 1 *The middle three digits are not 9*

If 100 is added, then the result is a palindrome

Case 2 *The middle three digits are all 9*

11 and 111 could be added to give another palindrome (11 could be too low except in traffic jams!)

Case 3 *The middle digit is 9 and the 2nd and 4th are not 9*

110 could be added to give another palindrome

So the possible distances are 11, 100, 110 and 111 miles.

Problem

A driver notices that her milometer is showing a 5 digit palindromic number. She is astonished when, two hours further on her travels, the milometer is showing another palindromic number.

Find the different possible numbers of miles that she could have travelled.

Solution 38

Problem

Teddy Bears

The Teddy Bears in the local toy hospital have been in the wars.

> 70% have lost an eye,
>
> 75% an ear,
>
> 80% an arm, and
>
> 85% a leg.

Find the minimum percentage of teddies that have lost all four.

Solution

Teddy Bears

From the figures given, 25% still have ears, 20% still have arms and 15% still have legs.

In a sample of 100, 70 have lost an eye.

Of those 70, 25 could still have both ears.

So at least 45 have lost an eye and an ear.

Of those 45, 20 could still have both arms.

So at least 25 have lost an eye, an ear and an arm.

Of those 25, 15 could still have both legs.

So at least 10 have lost an eye, an ear, an arm and a leg.

So the minimum percentage is 10%.

Problem

The Teddy Bears in the local toy hospital have been in the wars.

70% have lost an eye, 75% an ear, 80% an arm and 85% a leg.

Find the minimum percentage of teddies that have lost all four.

Solution 39

Problem

3D Pythagoras

Consider using Pythagoras Theorem in 3-dimensions.

For this, we get the general result that
$$a^2 + b^2 + c^2 = d^2.$$
One set of numbers that will satisfy this, is 2, 3, 6, 7 since $2^2 + 3^2 + 6^2 = 7^2$.

Another set is 5, 6, 30, 31 since $5^2 + 6^2 + 30^2 = 31^2$.

Show algebraically that, if you choose two consecutive whole numbers and their product they will form the three smallest numbers of such a set of numbers and say what the largest will be.

Solution

3D Pythagoras

Let the three numbers be n, $n + 1$ and $n(n + 1)$.

Squaring and adding gives

$$n^2 + (n + 1)^2 + n^2(n + 1)^2$$
$$= n^2 + n^2 + 2n + 1 + n^4 + 2n^3 + n^2$$
$$= n^4 + 2n^3 + 3n^2 + 2n + 1$$
$$= \left(n^2 + n + 1\right)^2$$

so these numbers fit the pattern.

As $n^2 + n + 1 = n(n + 1) + 1$, the largest number will always be one more than the product of the two smallest.

Problem

Consider using Pythagoras Theorem in 3-dimensions.

For this, we get the general result that

$$a^2 + b^2 + c^2 = d^2.$$

One set of numbers that will satisfy this, is 2, 3, 6, 7 since $2^2 + 3^2 + 6^2 = 7^2$.

Another set is 5, 6, 30, 31 since $5^2 + 6^2 + 30^2 = 31^2$.

Show algebraically that, if you choose two consecutive whole numbers and their product they will form the three smallest numbers of such a set of numbers and say what the largest will be.

Solution 40

Problem

Elevenses

A three digit number is such that its second digit is the sum of its first and third digits.

Prove that the number must be divisible by 11.

Can you find any 3 digit multiples of 11 that do not obey this rule?

Solution

Elevenses

If the number n has the digits a, b and c, then

$$n = 100a + 10b + c.$$

If $b = a + c$, then

$$
\begin{aligned}
n &= 100a + 10(a + c) + c \\
&= 100a + 10a + 10c + c \\
&= 110a + 11c \\
&= 11(10a + c)
\end{aligned}
$$

So n is divisible by 11.

209 is an example which does not obey this rule:

$$209 = 11 \times 19.$$

In this case, $b = a + c - 11$.

This shows that the converse of the result is false.

Problem

A three digit number is such that its second digit is the sum of its first and third digits.

Prove that the number must be divisible by 11.

Can you find any 3 digit multiples of 11 that do not obey this rule?

Solution 41

Problem

A Square and a Circle

In the diagram below, the square has side length 2.

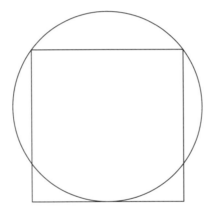

What is the radius of the circle?

Problem 42

Solution

A Square and a Circle

This proof uses similar triangles and the fact that the angle in a semi-circle is 90°.

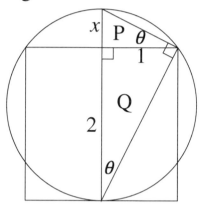

Triangles P and Q are similar, so

$$\tan \theta = \frac{x}{1} = \frac{1}{2}.$$

Therefore $x = \frac{1}{2}$.

Hence the diameter is 2½, so the radius is 1¼.

Problem

In the diagram below, the square has side length 2.

What is the radius of the circle?

Solution 42

Problem

Arcs

The shape below is made up of six joined quarter circle arcs, all of equal radius r.

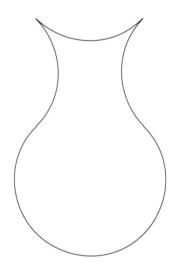

What is the area of the shape in terms of r?

Problem 43

Solution

Arcs

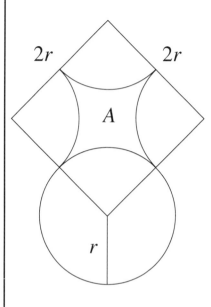

$2r$ $2r$

A

r

The area of A is $(2r)^2 - \pi r^2$
$= 4r^2 - \pi r^2$.

The area of the circle is πr^2.

So the required area is
$= 4r^2 - \pi r^2 + \pi r^2$
$= 4r^2$.

Note: the area is independent of π.

Problem

The shape below is made up of six joined quarter circle arcs, all of equal radius r.

What is the area of the shape in terms of r?

Solution 43

Problem

Find the angle

ABCD is a square.

E is the midpoint of *AB* and *F* is the midpoint of *BC*.

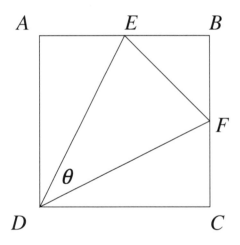

What is cos θ?

Problem 44

Solution

Find the angle

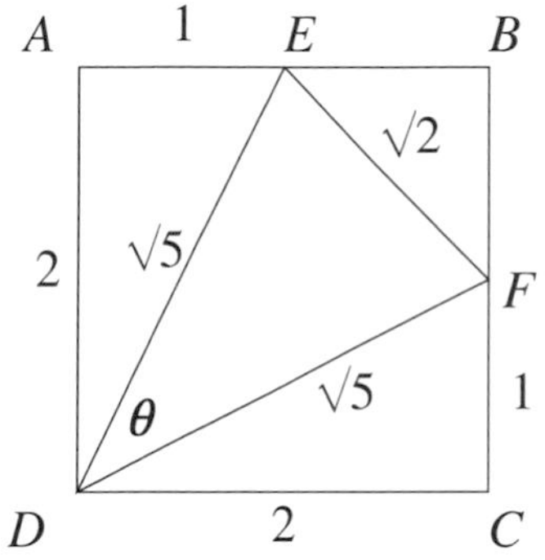

Let the square have side length 2 units. Then by Pythagoras' Theorem

$$DE = \sqrt{5} = DF$$

$$\text{and } EF = \sqrt{2}.$$

By the Cosine Rule

$$\cos\theta = \frac{(\sqrt{5})^2 + (\sqrt{5})^2 - (\sqrt{2})^2}{2 \times \sqrt{5} \times \sqrt{5}} = \frac{8}{10}$$

So, $\cos\theta = \dfrac{4}{5}.$

Problem

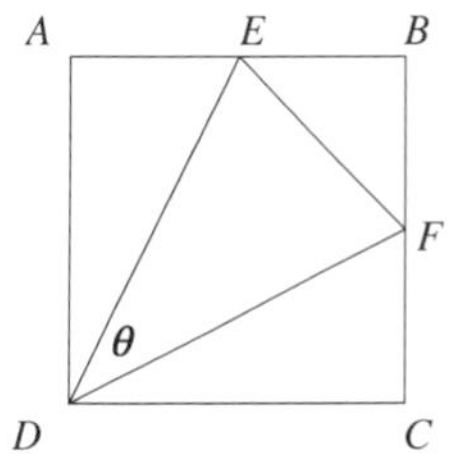

ABCD is a square.
E is the midpoint of *AB* and
F is the midpoint of *BC*.

What is $\cos\theta$?

Problem

Diagonal

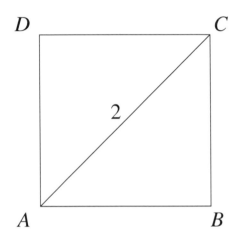

ABCD is a square with diagonal length 2.
What is its area?

If a square has diagonal length d, give a general formula for its area.

Problem 45

Solution

Diagonal

It is possible to solve the problem either pictorially, or algebraically using Pythagoras' Theorem:

Area of larger square = d^2.

So the area of $ABCD$ = $\dfrac{d^2}{2}$.

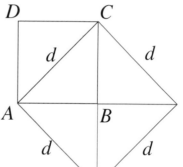

When $d = 2$, area = $\dfrac{2^2}{2} = 2$.

Or using Pythagoras' Theorem,

the length of one side of $ABCD$ is $\dfrac{d}{\sqrt{2}}$.

So, as before, the area is $\left(\dfrac{d}{\sqrt{2}}\right)^2 = \dfrac{d^2}{2}$.

Problem

$ABCD$ is a square with diagonal length 2.
What is its area?
If a square has diagonal length d, give a general formula for its area.

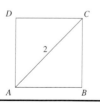

Solution 45

Problem

Win a car!

At a fair ground, a stall offers a prize of a car to the first person who can throw six sixes on six fair dice.

It costs 50p to have a go and the car costs the stall holder £5000.

What is the probability that the stall will make a profit? (Consider only the cost of the car.)

Problem 46

Solution

Win a car!

To make a profit the stall must take more than £5000 before the car is won.

This means that at least 10000 people must fail to get six sixes.

The probability of a profit is therefore the probability of **not** getting six sixes in 10000 attempts.

$$P(\text{six sixes}) = \left(\frac{1}{6}\right)^6 \Rightarrow P(\text{not six sixes}) = 1 - \left(\frac{1}{6}\right)^6$$

$$P(\text{not six sixes in 10000 throws})$$

$$= \left(1 - \left(\frac{1}{6}\right)^6\right)^{10000} = 0.807 \,(3 \text{ s.f.})$$

So the probability of the stall making a profit is 0.807 (3 sf)

Problem

At a fair ground, a stall offers a prize of a car to the first person who can throw six sixes on six fair dice.

It costs 50p to have a go and the car costs the stall holder £5000.

What is the probability that the stall will make a profit? (Consider only the cost of the car.)

Solution 46

Problem

Build a wall

To build a certain wall, a supervisor knows that these builders work at the following rates:

> a) Ali & Bill take 12 days
> b) Ali & Charlie take 15 days
> c) Bill & Charlie take 20 days

Assuming that the rates at which builders work are not affected by their companion:

1. How long would it take each of them working alone to build the wall?
2. How long would it take to build the wall if they all worked together?

Solution

Build a wall

Let a be the number of days it takes Ali to build the wall, so Ali builds $1/a$ of the wall each day.

Similarly, Bill builds $1/b$ and Charlie builds $1/c$ each day.

a) Since Ali and Bill build 1/12 of the wall each day $1/a + 1/b = 1/12$.

Similarly, $1/a + 1/c = 1/15$

and $1/b + 1/c = 1/20$.

Solving these three equations gives: $a = 20, b = 30, c = 60$.

b) Suppose that, working together, Ali, Bill & Charlie take x days,

then $1/x = 1/20 + 1/30 + 1/60$

$1/x = 3/60 + 2/60 + 1/60 = 6/60$

$x = 10$

So if they all work together they will take 10 days to build the wall.

Problem

To build a certain wall, a supervisor knows that these builders work at the following rates:

a) Ali & Bill take 12 days

b) Ali & Charlie take 15 days

c) Bill & Charlie take 20 days

Assuming that the rates at which builders work are not affected by their companion:

1. How long would it take each of them working alone to build the wall?

2. How long would it take to build the wall if they all worked together?

Solution 47

Problem

Find the missing number

$$6 \div 8 = 27$$

Insert the same number twice into the expression above to make it correct.

Problem 48

Solution

Find the missing number

Insert $\frac{1}{3}$ into the expression to make

$$6 \div 8^{\frac{1}{3}} = 27^{\frac{1}{3}}.$$

Remember that $8^{\frac{1}{3}}$ means the cube root of 8 which is 2 and $27^{\frac{1}{3}} = 3$.

So the expression becomes $6 \div 2 = 3$.

Another could be:

$$6 \div \frac{8}{6} = \frac{27}{6}.$$

But this solution involves putting in division signs as well.

Problem

$$6 \div 8 = 27$$

Insert the same number twice into the expression above to make it correct.

Solution 48

Problem

Complete the sequence

Look at the sequence below:

21
4221
63
84424221
105
12663

Suggest the next two numbers in the sequence, giving reasons.

Solution

Complete the sequence

The first digits in each of the terms are consecutive multiples of 21.

So the next two terms start : $\qquad$ 147 . . .

168 · · ·

The rest of the digits in each term are obtained by halving the first part of the term − this process is continued until an odd number is obtained.

So, the 7th term is **147** (it is odd)

For the 8th,

half of 168 is 84, so the term starts 16884.

half of 16884 is 8442, so the term starts 168848442,

half of this is 84424221 (which is odd)

So the 8th term is **16884844284424221.**

Problem

Look at the sequence below:

21   4221   63   84424221   105   12663

Suggest the next two numbers in the sequence, giving reasons.

Solution 49

Problem

Matches

Rectangular shapes are to be made from matchsticks.

Find an expression which gives the number of matchsticks needed, in terms of the area and the perimeter of the rectangle.

Problem 50

Solution

Matches

Each square in the rectangle is initially made from 2 matchsticks.

The number of squares equals the area of the rectangle.

To make up the completed shape, we need to put matchsticks down one width and across one length.

The total number of matchsticks is equal to

$$2(\text{Area}) + \tfrac{1}{2}(\text{Perimeter})$$

Problem

Rectangular shapes are to be made from matchsticks.

Find an expression which gives the number of matchsticks needed, in terms of the area and the perimeter of the rectangle.

Solution 50

Problem

Sums of Sequences

Consider the formulas:

$$\sum_{i=1}^{n} i = \frac{n(n+1)}{2}$$

and

$$\sum_{i=1}^{n} i^2 = \frac{n(n+1)(2n+1)}{6}$$

Explain why the results of these are always integers.

Solution

Sums of Sequences

The first result is trivial. If n is odd then $n + 1$ is even and divides exactly by 2 and, if n is even, it divides exactly by 2 so, in either case the product divides by 2 and there is no remainder.

The second result will always divide by 2 for the same reason so it needs to be shown that it also divides by 3.

If n is a multiple of 3 or if $n + 1$ is a multiple of 3 then the whole product divides by 3.

If neither n nor $n + 1$ divide by three then $n - 1$ must.

But $2n + 1 = 2(n - 1) + 3$, both parts of which are divisible by three so the product is again divisible by 3.

Problem

$$\sum_{i=1}^{n} i = \frac{n(n + 1)}{2} \quad \text{and} \quad \sum_{i=1}^{n} i^2 = \frac{n(n + 1)(2n + 1)}{6}$$

Explain why the results of these are always integers.

Solution 51

Problem

Similar Rectangles

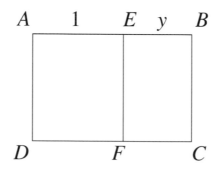

$ABCD$ is a rectangle with $AD = 1$ and $DC = x$ where $x = y + 1$.

$AEFD$ is a square.

$EBCF$ is a second rectangle similar to $ABCD$.

Find the exact value of x.

Solution

Similar Rectangles

ABCD is similar to *EBCF*.

So,
$$\frac{x}{1} = \frac{1}{x-1}$$

$\Rightarrow$ $\qquad x(x-1) = 1$

$\Rightarrow$ $\qquad x^2 - x - 1 = 0$

This gives the solution
$$x = \frac{1 + \sqrt{5}}{2}.$$

[Compare to Number 53].

Problem

ABCD is a rectangle with *AD* = 1 and *DC* = *x* where *x* = *y* + 1.

AEFD is a square.

EBCF is a second rectangle similar to *ABCD*.

Find the exact value of *x*.

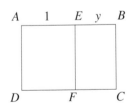

Solution 52

Problem

A diagonal of a pentagon

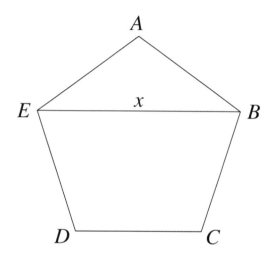

ABCDE is a regular pentagon of unit length.

Find the exact value of *x*.

Problem 53

Solution

A diagonal of a pentagon

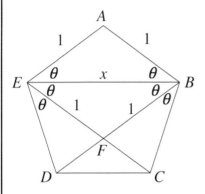

By symmetry,

$\angle AEB = \angle BEC = \angle CED = \angle ABE$ etc

$\triangle EFB \equiv \triangle EAB$, so $EF = 1 = BF$

$\angle EFB = \angle DFC$ (opposite angles)

$\angle FDC = \angle FCD = \theta$ (alternate angles)

So $\triangle FDC$ is similar to $\triangle EFB$.

$EC = x = BD$ and so $DF = x - 1 = FC$

This gives $\dfrac{x - 1}{1} = \dfrac{1}{x}$.

$\Rightarrow \quad x(x - 1) = 1$

$\Rightarrow \quad x^2 - x - 1 = 0$

This gives the solution

$$x = \frac{1 + \sqrt{5}}{2}$$

[Compare to Number 52]

Problem

ABCDE is a regular pentagon of unit length.

Find the exact value of *x*.

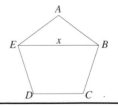

Solution 53

Problem

Happy Birthday!

What is the smallest number of people that it is necessary to have in a group so that the probability of at least two of them sharing the same birthday is greater than ½?

Problem 54

Solution

Happy Birthday!

The answer is 23.

Let n be the number of people in the group.

P(at least one pair with the same birthday)

$$= 1 - \text{P(no pairs)}$$

For one pair, P(different birthdays) $= \frac{364}{365}$

P(no pairs) $= \left(\frac{364}{365}\right)^p$ where $p = {}^nC_2 = \frac{n!}{(n-2)n!}$

(i.e. number of ways of choosing a pair)

We want P(no pairs) $\leqslant \frac{1}{2}$ (so P(at least one) $> \frac{1}{2}$).

$$\left(\frac{364}{365}\right)^p \leqslant \frac{1}{2}$$

Taking logs $\quad p \log \frac{364}{365} \leqslant \log \frac{1}{2}$

$$p \geqslant 252 \text{ as } \log \frac{364}{365} \leqslant 0.$$

$${}^{23}C_2 = 253, \text{ so } n = 23.$$

Problem

What is the smallest number of people that it is necessary to have in a group so that the probability of at least two of them sharing the same birthday is greater than ½?

Solution 54

Problem

A net of a cone

Consider a cone with base radius r and slant height l.

Prove that the curved surface area of the cone is
$A = \pi r l$.

Solution

A net of a cone

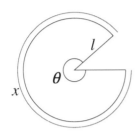

The net of a cone is a circle with a sector cut out.

The radius of the circle becomes l, the slant height of the cone.

The remaining circumference, x, becomes the circumference of the base of the cone.

So, for a cone, radius r, slant height l, curved surface area A.

$$x = l\theta = 2\pi r \Rightarrow \theta = \frac{2\pi r}{l}.$$

$$\text{So } A = \frac{\theta}{2\pi} \times \pi l^2$$

$$\Rightarrow A = \frac{2\pi r}{2\pi l} \times \pi l^2$$

$$\Rightarrow A = \pi r l.$$

Note: θ is measured in radians in the above working – it could be adapted for θ in degrees.

Problem

Consider a cone with base radius r and slant height l.

Prove that the curved surface area of the cone is $A = \pi r l$.

Solution 55

Problem

The Hands of Time

At 12 noon, the two hands of a clock are together.

When will be the next time that the hands are together?

Solution

The Hands of Time

After noon, there will be 11 more times, up to and including midnight, that the hands are together (effectively there is one time for every hour except 11 o'clock).

This means that the hands will be together every $\frac{12}{11}$ hours or 1 hour and $\frac{60}{11}$ minutes. ($\frac{60}{11}$ minutes = 5 minutes and 27 seconds.)

Therefore the next time will be
    1:05 pm and 27 seconds.

(Note this method works because the speeds of the hands are constant and so they will cross at constant intervals.)

Problem

At 12 noon, the two hands of a clock are together.

When will be the next time that the hands are together?

Solution 56

Problem

Primes

A *prime* number is a number which only has 2 factors.

Show that all prime numbers (except 2 and 3) can be written in the form

$$6n \pm 1.$$

Problem 57

Solution

Primes

Let p be a number ($p > 3$) and n be an appropriate integer.

Case 1: If $p = 6n$, then p would have a factor of 6 and so p could not be prime.

Case 2: If $p = 6n + 2$, then p would have a factor of 2 and so p could not be prime.

Case 3: If $p = 6n + 3$ then p would have a factor of 3 and so p could not be prime.

Case 4: If $p = 6n - 2$ then, as with Case 2, p would have a factor of 2 and so it could not be prime.

Hence, p could be prime only if it was of the form

$$6n + 1 \text{ or } 6n - 1.$$

(Note: the converse is *not* true, $25 = 6 \times 4 + 1$ is not prime.)

This is an example of *proof by exhaustion* – all the possible cases have been considered.

Problem

A *prime* number is a number which only has 2 factors.

Show that all prime numbers (except 2 and 3) can be written in the form $6n \pm 1$.

Solution 57

Problem

It all adds up

Look at the following calculations:

$$3 \times 1.5 = 4.5$$
$$5 \times 1.25 = 6.25$$
$$6 \times 1.2 = 7.2$$
$$11 \times 1.1 = 12.1$$

What is special about the numbers?

Problem 58

Solution

It all adds up

You obtain the same answer whether you add or multiply the first two numbers.

$$3 \times 1{\cdot}5 = 4{\cdot}5 = 3 + 1{\cdot}5$$
$$5 \times 1{\cdot}25 = 6{\cdot}25 = 5 + 1{\cdot}25$$
$$6 \times 1{\cdot}2 = 7{\cdot}2 = 6 + 1{\cdot}2$$
$$11 \times 1{\cdot}1 = \qquad = 11 + 1{\cdot}1$$

There is an infinite number of examples.

Generally, if the first number is n, then the second number is of the form

$$\frac{n}{n-1} = 1 + \frac{1}{n-1}.$$

See if you can prove this.

Problem

Look at the following calculations:

$3 \times 1{\cdot}5 = 4{\cdot}5$; $5 \times 1{\cdot}25 = 6{\cdot}25$; $6 \times 1{\cdot}2 = 7{\cdot}2$; $11 \times 1{\cdot}1 = 12{\cdot}1$

What is special about the numbers?

Solution 58

Problem

Turning

Emma is standing near a church and a big oak tree.

Initially, she faces the church. To face the oak tree she has to turn through an angle of 40°.

If T is the tree and C is the church, draw the locus of all the possible points of where Emma could be standing.

• T

• C

Problem 59

Solution

Turning

The locus of points looks like this:

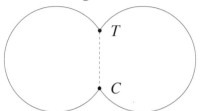

(*C* stands for the position of the church and *T* for the tree.)

The locus consists of 2 circular arcs – this is due to the circle theorem that says all angles subtended by an arc are equal.

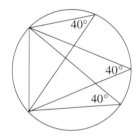

Note: if the angle in the question was 90°, then the locus would be a circle.

Problem

Emma is standing near a church and a big oak tree. Initially, she faces the church. To face the oak tree she has to turn through an angle of 40°.

If *T* is the tree and *C* is the church, draw the locus of all the possible points of where Emma could be standing.

• *T*

• *C*

Solution 59

Problem

Sixes

What is the probability of an odd number of sixes turing up in a random throw of *n* fair dice?

Solution

Sixes

Let P be the probability of an odd number of sixes.

$P = P(1 \text{ six}) + P(3 \text{ sixes}) + P(5 \text{ sixes}) + \ldots$

$$= \binom{n}{1}\left(\frac{5}{6}\right)^{n-1}\left(\frac{1}{6}\right) + \binom{n}{3}\left(\frac{5}{6}\right)^{n-3}\left(\frac{1}{6}\right)^3 + \binom{n}{5}\left(\frac{5}{6}\right)^{n-5}\left(\frac{1}{6}\right)^5 + \ldots$$

This equals the sum of the even-ranked terms in the expression

$$\left(\frac{5}{6} + \frac{1}{6}\right)^6.$$

To cancel out the odd terms use: $\left(\frac{5}{6} - \frac{1}{6}\right)^6$. In this expression the even-ranked terms are negative.

$$P = \tfrac{1}{2}\left[\left(\tfrac{5}{6} + \tfrac{1}{6}\right)^6 - \left(\tfrac{5}{6} - \tfrac{1}{6}\right)^6\right] = \tfrac{1}{2}\left[(1)^n - \left(\tfrac{2}{3}\right)^n\right] = \tfrac{1}{2}\left[1 - \left(\tfrac{2}{3}\right)^n\right]$$

Problem

What is the probability of an odd number of sixes turing up in a random throw of n fair dice?

Solution 60

Problem

The Truel

A truel is similar to a duel, except there are three people involved instead of two. Annie, Beryl and Claire decide to truel with pistols until only one survives.

Annie is the worst shot – she has a one in three chance of hitting the target.

Beryl is better, having a two in three chance of hitting her target.

Claire hits her target every time.

To make the truel fairer they take it in turns to shoot, with Annie having first shot, followed by Beryl if she is still alive and then Claire, if she is still alive and then round again.

Where should Annie aim her first shot?

Problem 61

Solution

The Truel

Annie should aim in the air — then Beryl will aim at Claire, as being the greater risk.

If Beryl misses Claire, Claire will aim for Beryl as being the greater danger and as Claire always hits her target, just Annie and Claire will be left.

If Beryl hits Claire, then just Annie and Beryl will be left.

In both cases, just 2 people (Annie and one other) will be left, with Annie having the first shot.

Note: This problem is concerned with a branch of Mathematics called *Game Theory*.

Problem

A truel is similar to a duel, except there are three people involved instead of two. Annie, Beryl and Claire decide to truel with pistols until only one survives.

Annie is the worst shot — she has a one in three chance of hitting the target.

Beryl is better, having a two in three chance of hitting her target.

Claire hits her target every time.

To make the truel fairer they take it in turns to shoot, with Annie having first shot, followed by Beryl if she is still alive and then Claire, if she is still alive and then round again.

Where should Annie aim her first shot?

Solution 61

Problem

The Quiz Show

A winning contestant in a quiz show is invited to choose one of three doors to select her prize. She will receive whatever is behind her chosen door. Behind one door is an expensive sports car and behind each of the other two doors is a goat.

The contestant chooses a door. The quiz show host then opens one of the doors which was not chosen and reveals a goat. The host then invites the contestant to change her mind and choose the other door, if she so wishes.

What is the contestant's best strategy?

Should she stick with her original choice, or should she change her mind, or does it make no difference to her chance of winning the car?

Problem 62

Solution

The Quiz Show

One way to approach the problem is to simulate it on a computer, either by using a spreadsheet or a simple program.

A simulation would show that the contestant will, on average, double her chances of winning the car if she chooses to change her mind. (This goes against most people's intuition.)

Initially, the probability of each door concealing the car is $\frac{1}{3}$, so the probability of a contestant being correct is $\frac{1}{3}$ and the probability of the other two doors being correct is $\frac{2}{3}$ between them.

Once you know which of these doors is definitely incorrect (there is a goat behind it), the other door that was not chosen now carries the whole of this $\frac{2}{3}$ probability of being correct, since the probability that the car is behind the door which the host allows you to see behind is 0.

Problem

A winning contestant in a quiz show is invited to choose one of three doors to select her prize. She will receive whatever is behind her chosen door. Behind one door is an expensive sports car and behind each of the other two doors is a goat.

The contestant chooses a door. The quiz show host then opens one of the doors which was not chosen and reveals a goat. The host then invites the contestant to change her mind and choose the other door, if she so wishes.

What is the contestant's best strategy?

Should she stick with her original choice, or should she change her mind, or does it make no difference to her chance of winning the car?

Solution 62

Appendix

In a few cases, alternative solutions were considered and these appear below.

Problem

Van Schooten

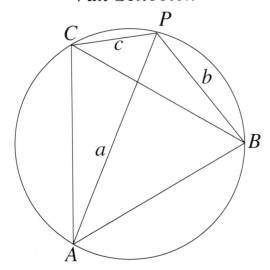

ABC is an equilateral triangle inscribed in a circle.

P is a point on the minor arc BC.

If $AP = a$, $BP = b$, $CP = c$, prove $a = b + c$ (Van Schooten's Theorem).

Problem 33

Solution

Van Schooten

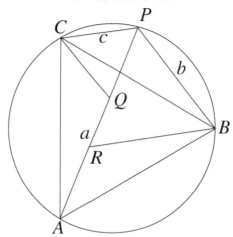

$\angle APB = \angle ACB = 60°$ (angles in the same segment)

Similarly, $\angle APC = 60° = \angle ABC$.

Now draw a line CQ to make $\triangle CPQ$ equilateral and another line, BR, to make $\triangle BPR$ equilateral. Then $\angle CQP = 60° = \angle ACQ + \angle QAC$ but $\angle BAR + \angle CAR = 60°$ thus $\angle BAR = \angle ACQ$ and $\angle ARB = \angle AQC\,(= 120°)$ and $AB = AC$. So $\triangle CQA$ and $\triangle ARB$ are congruent.

Thus $AR = CQ = c$ and so because $PR = b$ it is seen that $a = b + c$.

Solution

Arcs

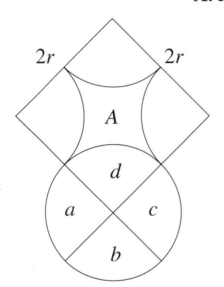

2r   2r

A

d

a   c

b

The quarter circles a, b and c fit into the square (d staying where it is). So the shape has the same area as the square i.e. $4r^2$.

Note: the area is independent of π.

Problem 43

The shape below is made up of six joined quarter circle arcs, all of equal radius r.

What is the area of the shape in terms of r?

Solution

Find the area

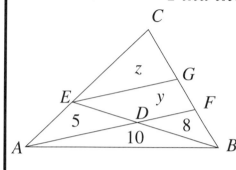

G is constructed so that EG is parallel to AF and $x = y + z$ as shown.

$BD = \frac{10}{15}BE = \frac{2}{3}BE$
$\Rightarrow$
$\triangle BDF = \frac{4}{9}\triangle BEG$.
Hence
$\frac{4}{9}(y + 8) = 8$ so
$y = 10$.

$EG = \frac{3}{2}DF$ and $DF = \frac{8}{18}AF \Rightarrow EG = \frac{2}{3}AF \Rightarrow$
$\triangle CEG = \frac{4}{9}\triangle CAF$.
$\frac{4}{9}(y + z + 5) = z$ giving $\frac{4}{9}(z + 15) = z$, since
$y = 10$. Thus $z = 12$ and so, $x = y + z = 22$.

Problem 34

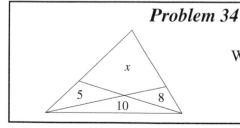

What is the area x?

Pig and Other Tales

– A Book of Mathematical Readings

ISBN 0 906588 38 3

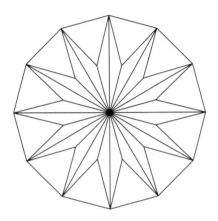

The readings in this book have been chosen from past issues of the *Mathematical Gazette*, since it was felt that they could profitably be studied by A level and Scottish Higher Mathematics students. They cover a wide variety of topics, and whilst some are more difficult to understand than others, most should be accessible to the majority of such students.

The readings are accompanied by questions on their content. The questions are structured to help the student get the most out of each reading. The skill of reading and understanding mathematical or scientific articles is an important one, and is not one that is generally addressed.